Contents

Numbers 1 - 10 ………………………………… 1

The teddy bear's picnic …………………… 8

Greetings & essential words …………… 14

Toys …………………………………… 20

Colours ……………………………… 24

A trip to the beach ………………… 32

Ice creams ………………………… 36

Zoo animals ……………………… 38

French - English word list …………… 41

Board game style game…………… 44

Answers …………………………… 46

un

deux

trois

quatre

cinq

Read the French numbers
as you colour the teddies.

How many fish are there?

Write the number of fish in French:

a)

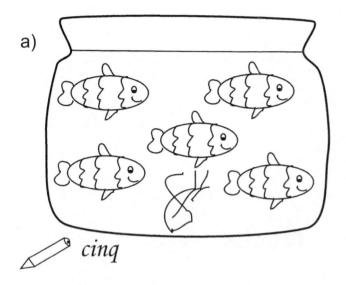

cinq

_____

b)

_____

c)

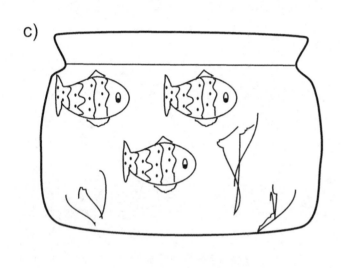

_____

d)

_____

e)

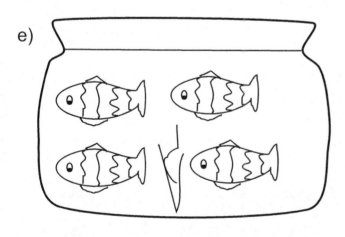

1 = un
2 = deux
3 = trois
4 = quatre
5 = cinq

_____

2

The fish are missing!

Can you draw the correct number of fish in each fish tank?:

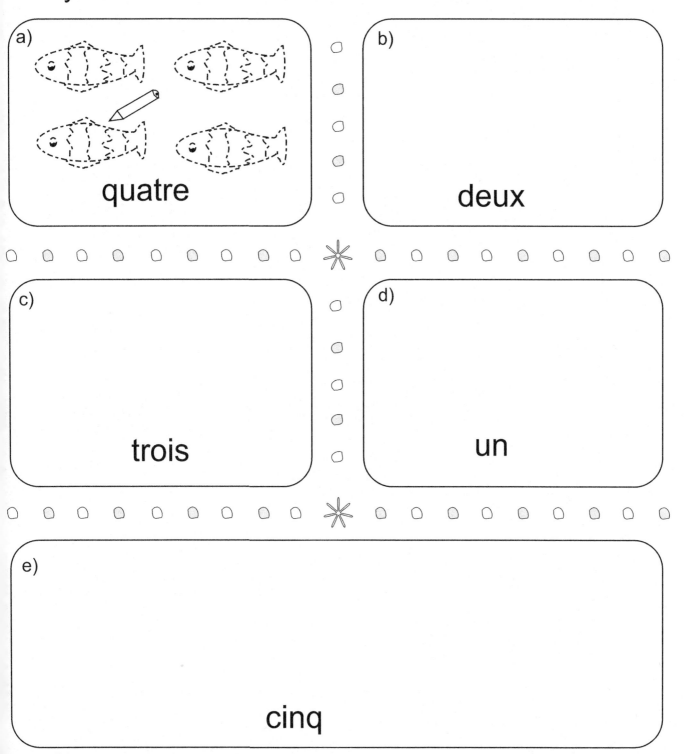

a) quatre

b) deux

c) trois

d) un

e) cinq

1	2	3	4	5
un	deux	trois	quatre	cinq

Numbers 6 - 10

Colour the balloons as you read the French numbers:

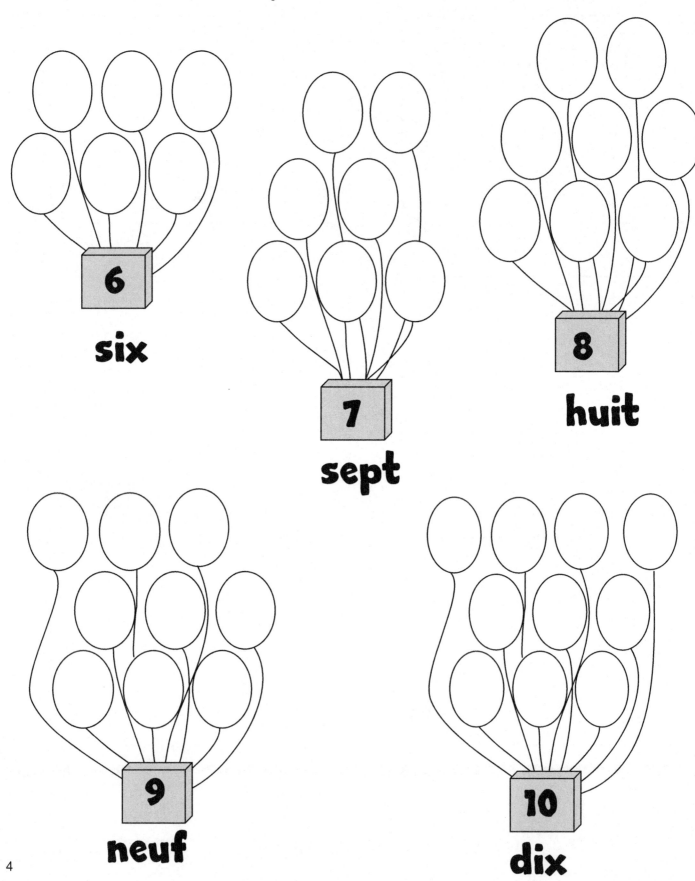

six

sept

huit

neuf

dix

How many are there?

Count the sweets and write the number in French:

a)

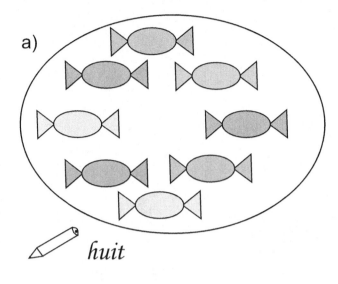

huit

_____

b)

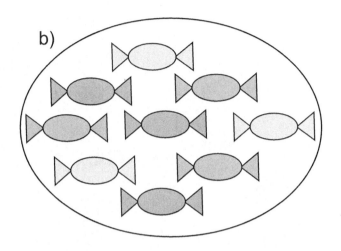

_____

c)

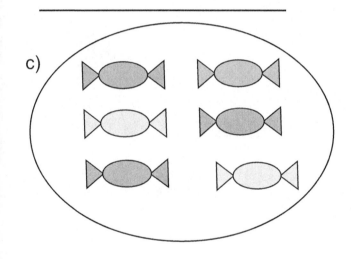

_____

d)

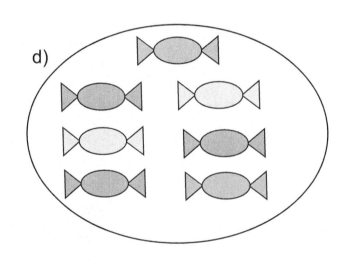

_____

e)

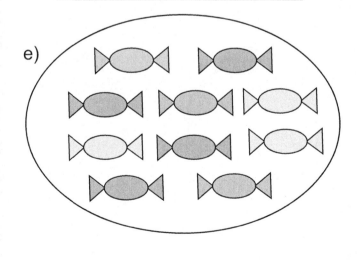

_____

6 = six

7 = sept

8 = huit

9 = neuf

10 = dix

Colour the odd numbers:

The odd numbers are as follows:
un   trois   cinq   sept   neuf

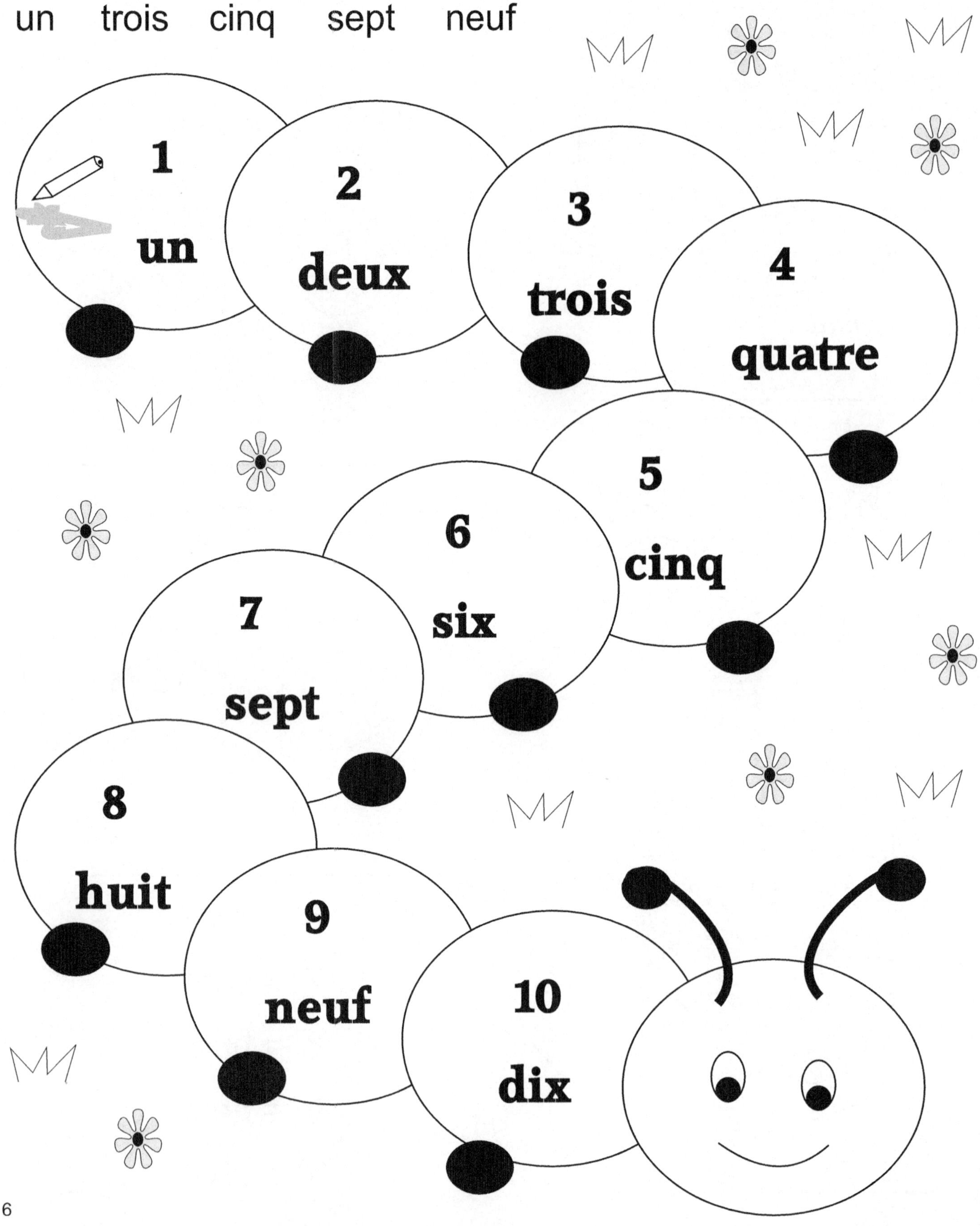

1 un

2 deux

3 trois

4 quatre

5 cinq

6 six

7 sept

8 huit

9 neuf

10 dix

Numbers 1 - 10

U	N	I	O	P	N	M	R	R	T
X	W	D	E	U	X	K	L	C	T
W	R	T	I	K	T	R	O	I	S
W	C	I	N	Q	B	H	J	L	C
Q	W	T	Y	I	P	S	E	P	T
U	D	S	Y	H	K	I	L	P	Y
A	W	I	U	O	H	U	I	T	X
T	Z	X	A	T	I	K	L	P	M
R	C	F	N	E	U	F	Y	I	P
E	D	T	Y	I	X	E	D	I	X

Find the following words:

1	2	3	4	5
UN	DEUX	TROIS	QUATRE	CINQ

6	7	8	9	10
SIX	SEPT	HUIT	NEUF	DIX

The teddy bear's picnic

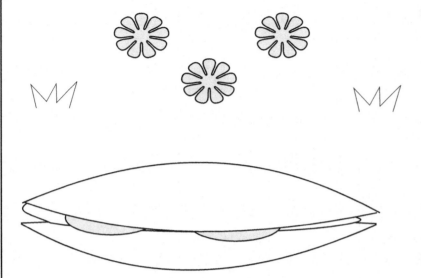

un nounours

un sandwich

un jus d'orange

une pomme

Colour the pictures as you read the French words.

What is it called in French?

Draw a line from the object to the correct French word:

un nounours

un jus d'orange

un sandwich

une pomme

un nounours   un jus d'orange   un sandwich   une pomme

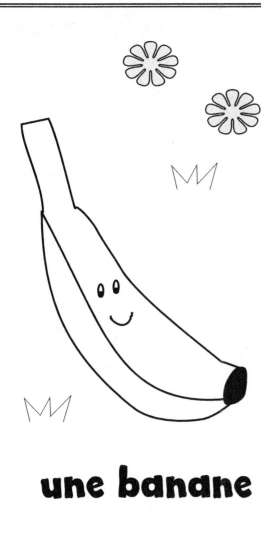

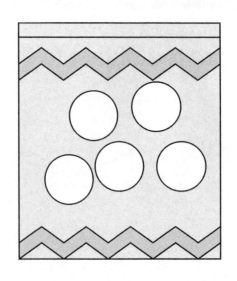

des chips

une banane

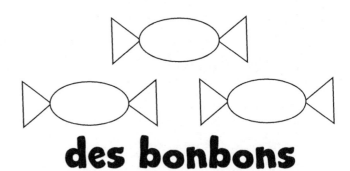

des bonbons

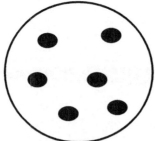

des biscuits

10

Which French word is it?

Circle the correct word:

1) une pomme | une banane

2) des chips | une banane

3) des chips | des biscuits

4) des bonbons | des chips

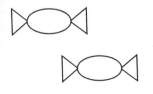
des bonbons

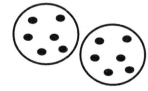
des biscuits

des chips

une banane

A teddy bear is having a picnic!

Imagine you are going to the teddy bear's picnic.
Tick (✓)the items you would like to have.

	un nounours	✓
	un sandwich	
	un jus d'orange	
	une banane	
	une pomme	
	des biscuits	
	des bonbons	
	des chips	

═ Draw the following things: ═

1) un sandwich

2) un nounours

3) une pomme

4) une banane

5) des biscuits

6) des bonbons

 un sandwich un nounours une pomme une banane des biscuits 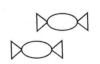 des bonbons

13

Saying hello!

Write **Bonjour** (Hello) in the space provided:

Saying goodbye!

Write **Au revoir** (Goodbye) in the space provided:

Introducing yourself!

Introduce yourself by writing Je m'appelle and then write your name.   (Je m'appelle = My name is)

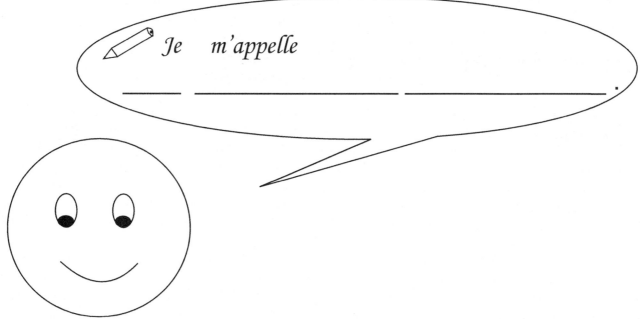

Essential words

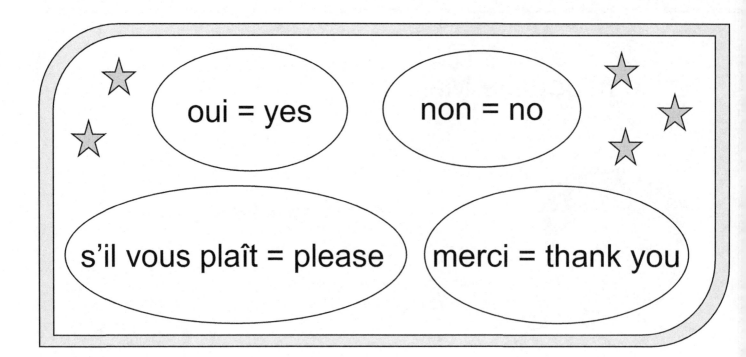

oui = yes

non = no

s'il vous plaît = please

merci = thank you

How do you say the following in French?

Fill in the missing letters:

1) yes   o u __

2) thank you   m e r __ __

3) no   __ o __

4) please   s'il __ __ __ __ plaît

Comment ça va? (How are you?)

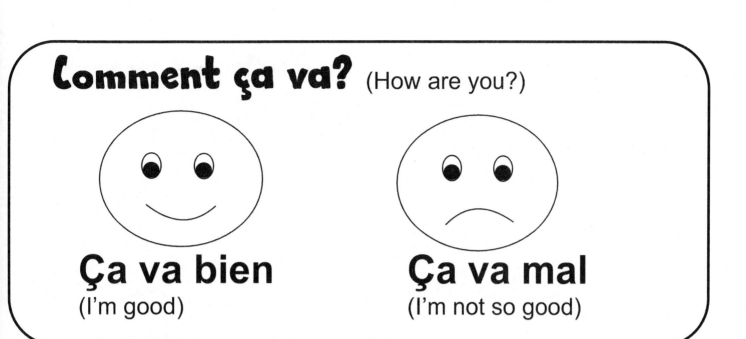

Ça va bien
(I'm good)

Ça va mal
(I'm not so good)

Look at the pictures and complete the sentences using either **bien** (good) or **mal** (not so good).

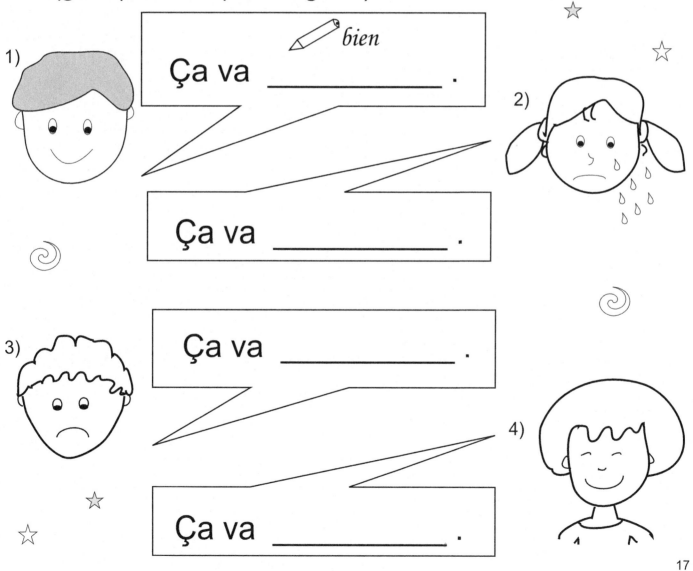

1) Ça va _bien_ _____ .

Ça va _____ .

2)

3) Ça va _____ .

Ça va _____ .

4)

What is it in French?

Draw a line from the English to the French words:

Hello

My name is

I'm good

yes

thank you

Good bye

Ça va bien

merci

Bonjour

Au revoir

Je m'appelle

oui

Word search

B	O	N	J	O	U	R	D	E	I	B	N
G	H	K	L	O	M	E	R	C	I	X	O
O	E	P	O	M	M	E	M	L	I	C	N
U	W	E	T	B	O	N	B	O	N	S	Y
I	S	F	J	K	L	P	O	T	Y	C	S
W	Q	J	E	M'	A	P	P	E	L	L	E
Y	H	L	O	P	B	V	F	G	H	K	I
S'	I	L	V	O	U	S	P	L	A	Î	T
Z	E	R	T	N	O	U	N	O	U	R	S
S'	A	U	R	E	V	O	I	R	M	I	K

Find the following words:

BONJOUR   MERCI   OUI

AU REVOIR   POMME   NON

JE M'APPELLE   BONBONS

S'IL VOUS PLAÎT   NOUNOURS

Toys

Read the French words
as you colour the pictures:

un train

une poupée

un ballon

un bateau

Which toy is it?

Draw the pictures and copy the French words:

1) une poupée

_____

2) un ballon

_____

3) un bateau

_____

4) un train

_____

une poupée

un ballon

un bateau

un train

Which picture is it?

Draw a line from the French word to the correct picture:

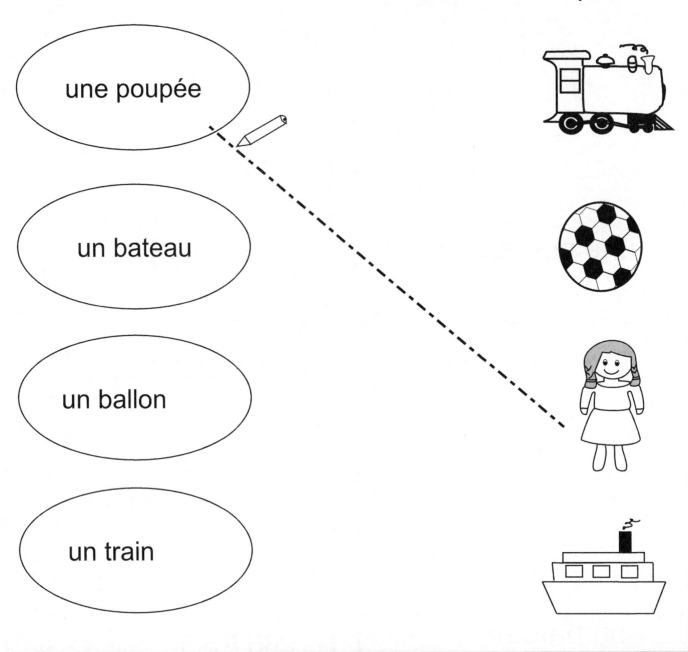

une poupée

un bateau

un ballon

un train

une poupée   un ballon   un train   un bateau

Which letters are missing?

1) un ba___on

2) un ___ain

3) une p___pé___

4) un bat_____

Colours

rouge

Colour the pictures using the correct colours:

rouge - red

jaune - yellow

vert - green

24

jaune

vert

What colour is it?

Write the colour of the object in French:

 *rouge*

1) _____

2) 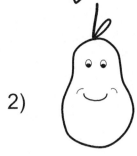 _____

3)  _____

4)  _____

5)  _____

6) 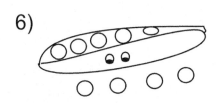 _____

rouge - red   jaune - yellow   vert - green

Colour the pictures using the correct colours:

marron
(brown)

rose
(pink)

bleu
(blue)

What colour is it?

Write the colour of the object in French:

rose - pink   marron - brown   bleu - blue

1)

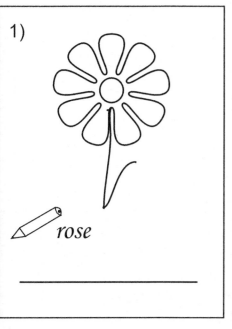

rose

_____

2)

_____

3)

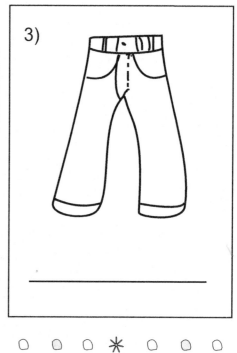

_____

4)

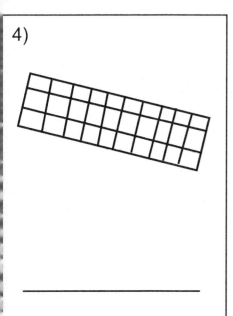

_____

5)

_____

6)

_____

What colour is it?

Colour the pictures using
the correct colours:

rose

jaune

vert

bleu

marron

marron

rouge

rose

Draw a line between the colour the correct picture:

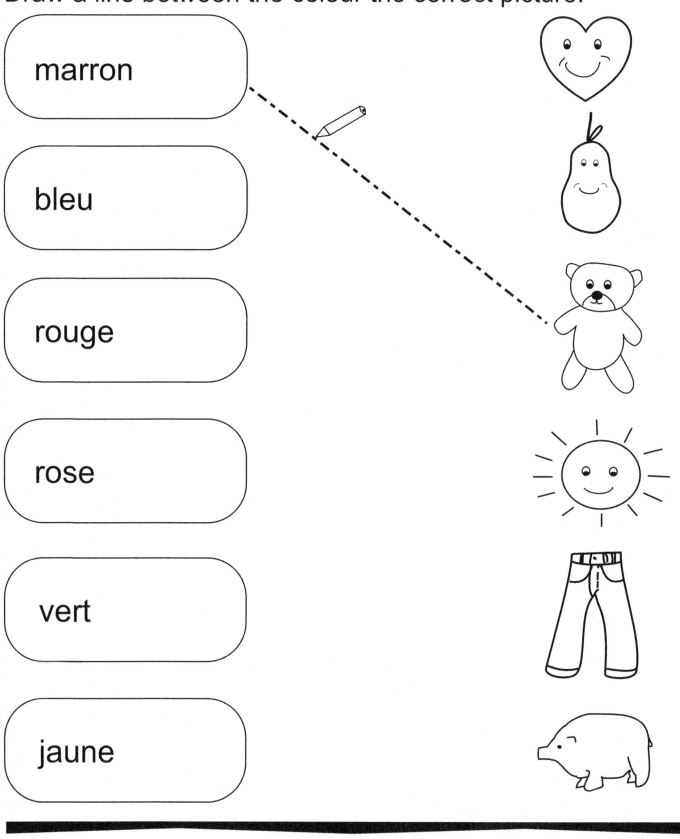

marron

bleu

rouge

rose

vert

jaune

marron - brown   bleu - blue   rouge - red

rose - pink   vert - green   jaune - yellow

Colour the pictures using the correct colours:

violet

(lilac)

blanc

(white)

gris

(grey)

noir

(black)

orange

(orange)

Complete the words for the French colours:

1)

 o   i

n __ __ r

2)

__ __ a n c

3)

__ i o __ __ __

4)

o r __ __ g e

5)

g r __ __

noir - black   blanc - white   violet - lilac

orange - orange   gris - grey

A trip to the beach!

Read the French words as you colour the pictures:

le soleil

la plage

(the beach)

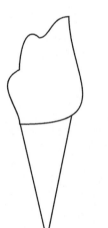

une glace

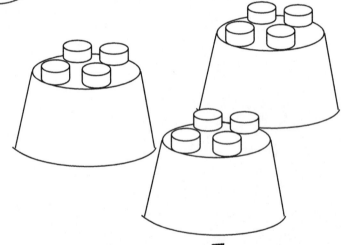

un château

la mer

What is it?

Read the French words and draw a picture:

1)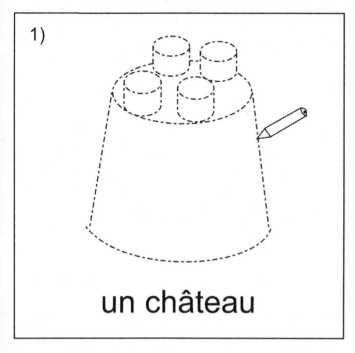

un château

2)

une glace

3)

le soleil

4)

la mer

le soleil

la mer

une glace

un château

Which word is it?

Draw a line between the pictures and the French words:

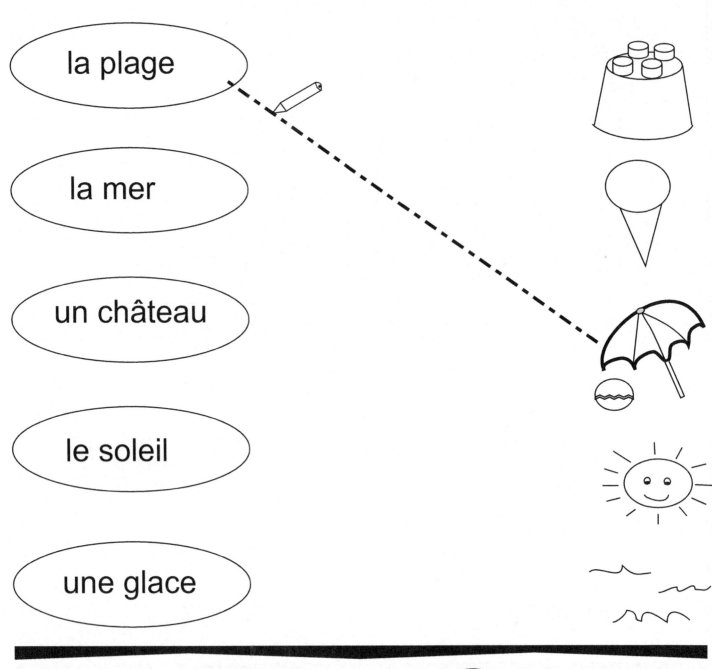

la plage

la mer

un château

le soleil

une glace

le soleil   la plage   la mer   une glace   un château

Circle the correct word

1)  la mer   une glace   un château

2)  le soleil   la plage   la mer

3) 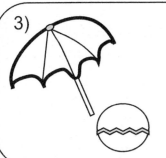 la mer   le soleil   la plage

4) 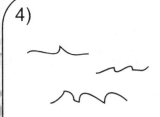 la plage   la mer   le soleil

5) 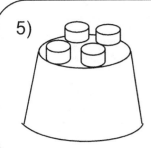 une glace   un château   la mer

Ice cream flavours

Colour the ice creams in the correct colour:

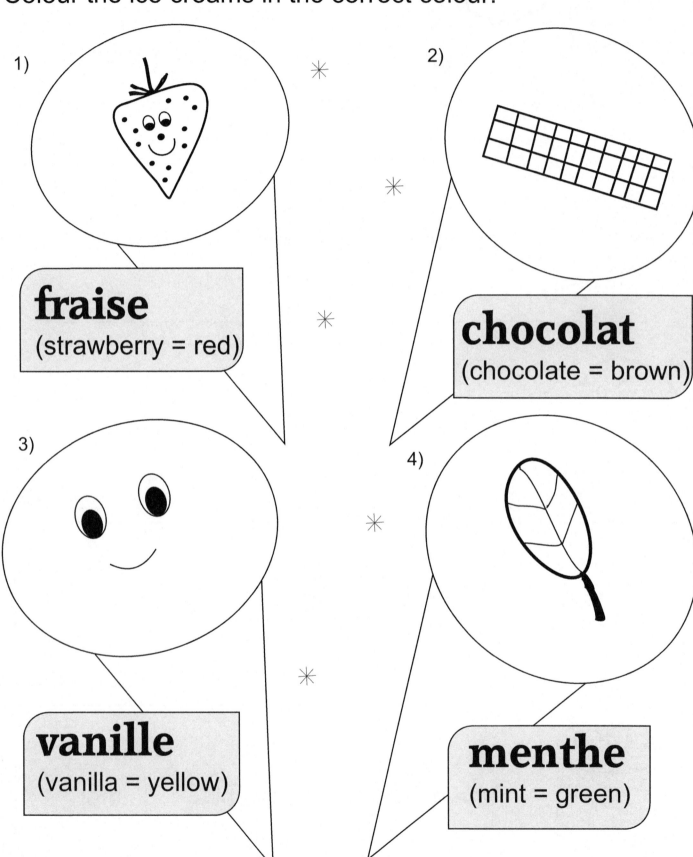

1)

fraise
(strawberry = red)

2)

chocolat
(chocolate = brown)

3)

vanille
(vanilla = yellow)

4)

menthe
(mint = green)

Colour the ice cream using the correct colours:

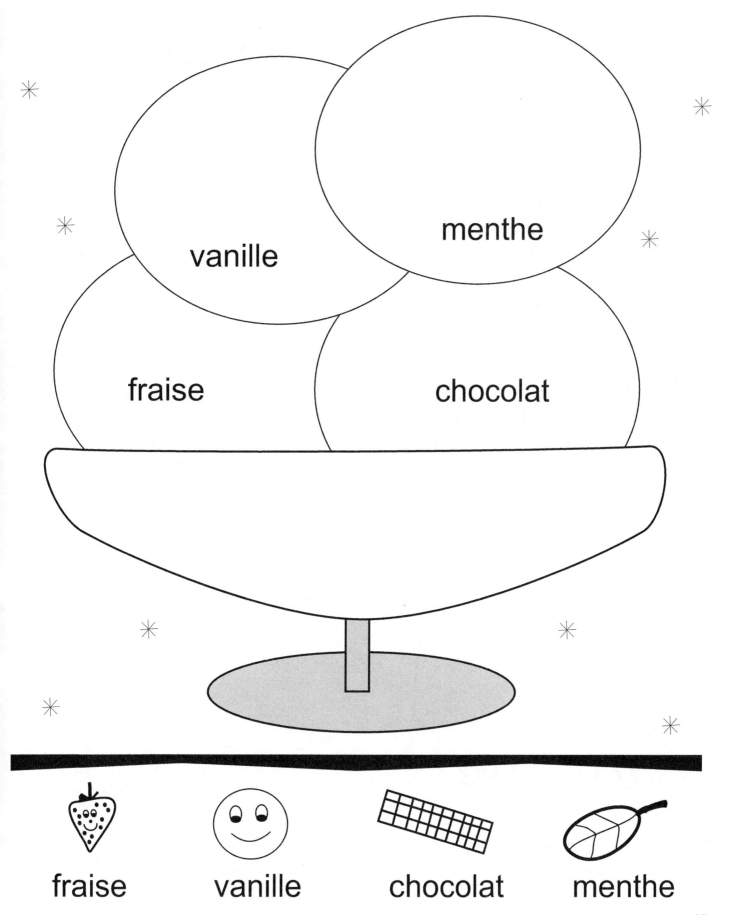

fraise   vanille   chocolat   menthe

Colour the animals as you read the French words:

une girafe

un éléphant

un lion

un serpent

What animal is it?

Write the French words for the animals:

1)

une girafe

2)

3)

4)

une girafe   un éléphant   un lion   un serpent

Word search

 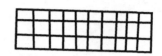 

V	A	N	I	L	L	E	T	I	P	W	S
X	G	C	H	O	C	O	L	A	T	M	E
M	W	T	U	I	P	K	J	N	C	D	R
E	I	L	K	F	R	A	I	S	E	L	P
N	Z	I	J	L	I	O	N	V	X	F	E
T	E	O	T	G	I	R	A	F	E	P	N
H	B	N	M	K	X	F	W	Z	A	J	T
E	U	Y	É	L	É	P	H	A	N	T	A

Find the following words:

FRAISE   LION

VANILLE   GIRAFE

CHOCOLAT   SERPENT

MENTHE   ÉLÉPHANT

French		English	
	Au revoir		Good bye
un	ballon	a	ball
une	banane	a	banana
un	bateau	a	boat
des	biscuits	some	biscuits
	blanc		white
	bleu		blue
des	bonbons	some	sweets
	Bonjour		Hello
	Ça va bien		I'm good
	Ça va mal		I'm not so good
un	château	a	castle
des	chips	some	crisps
	chocolat		chocolate
	cinq		five
	deux		two
	dix		ten
un	éléphant	an	elephant
	fraise		strawberry
une	girafe	a	giraffe
une	glace	an	ice cream
	gris		grey
	huit		eight
	jaune		yellow
	Je m'appelle		My name is
un	jus d'orange	an	orange juice
un	lion	a	lion
	marron		brown

French		English	
	menthe		mint
	merci		thank you
la	mer	the	sea
	neuf		nine
	noir		black
	non		no
un	nounours	a	teddy bear
	orange		orange
	oui		yes
la	plage	the	beach
une	pomme	an	apple
une	poupée	a	doll
	quatre		four
	rose		pink
	rouge		red
un	sandwich	a	sandwich
	sept		seven
un	serpent	a	snake
	s'il vous plaît		please
	six		six
le	soleil	the	sun
un	train	a	train
	trois		three
	un		one
	vanille		vanilla
	vert		green
	violet		lilac

Numbers 1 - 10

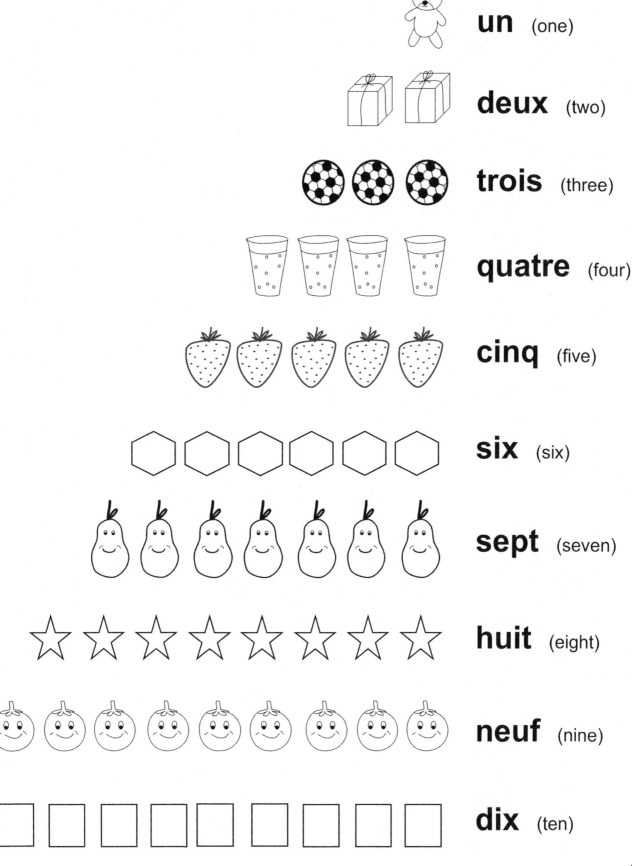

un (one)

deux (two)

trois (three)

quatre (four)

cinq (five)

six (six)

sept (seven)

huit (eight)

neuf (nine)

dix (ten)

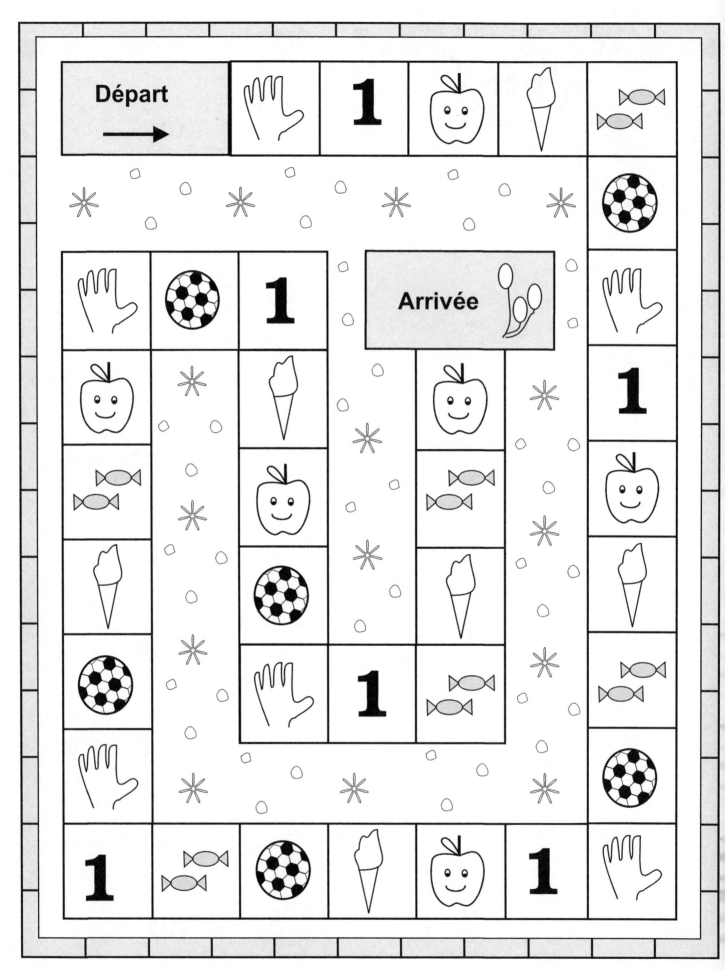

Départ →

Arrivée

44

French Word Game

For this game, you will need a dice and a counter for each player. The counters could be rubbers, cubes or you could make your own on pieces of paper.

How to play

Start at **Départ,** roll the dice and count that number of squares.

Say the word in French for the picture you land on.

To win, arrive first at **Arrivée**

Bonjour
(Hello)

un
(one)

un ballon
(a ball)

une pomme
(an apple)

une glace
(an ice cream)

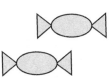

des bonbons
(some sweets)

 Games are a fun way to learn a foreign language! If you like games you could try the book French Word Games - Cool Kids Speak French

Answers

Page 2

a) cinq
b) un
c) trois
d) deux
e) quatre

Page 3

The following number of
fish should be drawn:
a) 4   d) 1
b) 2   e) 5
c) 3

Page 5

a) huit
b) neuf
c) six
d) sept
e) dix

Page 6

The odd numbers
should have been
coloured:

1, 3, 5, 7 & 9

Page 7

Page 9

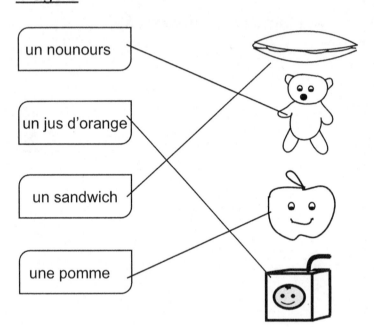

un nounours

un jus d'orange

un sandwich

une pomme

Page 11

1) une banane   2) des chips   3) des biscuits   4) des bonbons

Page 13

The following should be drawn:
1) a sandwich
2) a teddy
3) an apple
4) a banana
5) biscuits
6) sweets

Page 16

1) oui
2) merci
3) non
4) s'il vous plaît

Page 17

1) Ça va bien
2) Ça va mal
3) Ça va mal
4) Ça va bien

Page 18

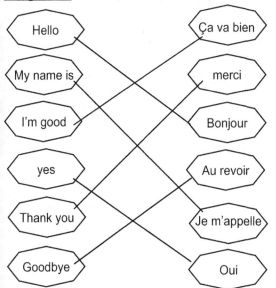

Hello
My name is
I'm good
yes
Thank you
Goodbye

Ça va bien
merci
Bonjour
Au revoir
Je m'appelle
Oui

Page 19

B	O	N	J	O	U	R				N
				M	E	R	C	I		O
O		P	O	M	M	E				N
U			B	O	N	B	O	N	S	
I										
	J	E	M'	A	P	P	E	L	L	E
S'	I	L	V	O	U	S	P	L	A	Î	T
	N	O	U	N	O	U	R	S		
A	U	R	E	V	O	I	R			

Page 21

The following
should be drawn
1) a doll
2) a ball
3) a boat
4) a train

Page 22

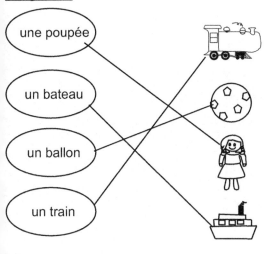

une poupée
un bateau
un ballon
un train

Page 23

1) un ballon
2) un train
3) une poupée
4) un bateau

Page 24

rouge = red
jaune = yellow
vert = green

Page 25

1) rouge
2) vert
3) jaune
4) rouge
5) jaune
6) vert

Page 26

marron = brown
rose = pink
bleu = blue

Page 27

1) rose
2) marron
3) bleu
4) marron
5) bleu
6) rose

Page 28

rose = pink
jaune = yellow
vert = green
marron = brown
bleu = blue
rouge = red
rose = pink

Page 29

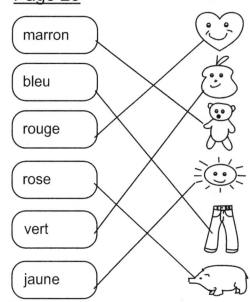

marron
bleu
rouge
rose
vert
jaune

Page 31

1) noir
2) blanc
3) violet
4) orange
5) gris

Page 33

The following things should be drawn:
1) a castle
2) an ice cream
3) the sun
4) the sea

Page 34

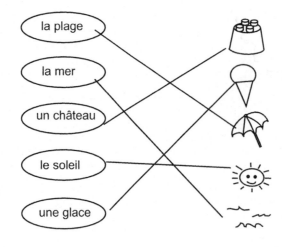

Page 35

1) une glace
2) le soleil
3) la plage
4) la mer
5) un château

Page 36

The ice creams should be:
1) red
2) brown
3) yellow
4) green

Page 37
vanille = yellow
menthe = green
fraise = red
chocolat = brown

Page 39
1) une girafe
2) un lion
3) un serpent
4) un éléphant

Page 40

V	A	N	I	L	L	E				S
		C	H	O	C	O	L	A	T	E
M										R
E		L		F	R	A	I	S	E	P
N		I								E
T		O		G	I	R	A	F	E	N
H		N								T
E			É	L	É	P	H	A	N	T

I hope you have enjoyed the fun activities in this book! Try to look back at the French words from time to time to help you remember them. Reviews help other readers discover my books so please consider leaving a short review on the site where the book was purchased. Your feedback is important to me. Thank you! And have fun learning French! It's a lovely language to learn! Joanne Leyland

For more information about learning French and the great books by Joanne Leyland go to **https://funfrenchforkids.com**

For information about learning French, Spanish, German, Italian or English as a foreign language go to **https://learnforeignwords.com**

For children under 7 there are also the following books by Joanne Leyland:

Daniel And The French Robot
Books 1, 2 & 3

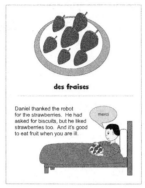

In each book there are 2 great stories. The French robot introduces / reinforces French words within an English storyline. At the back of the book is a French vocabulary page.

Jack And The French Languasaurus
Books 1, 2 & 3

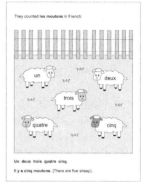

Have fun learning your first words in French with the French dinosaur! Each book has two brilliant stories and a French vocabulary page at the end. Ideal for 3-7 year olds.

Sophie And The French Magician

With two fantastic stories in each book. The French magician introduces / reinforces French words within an English storyline. French vocabulary page at end of book.

French Colouring Book For Kids Ages 5 - 7

The 10 topics include: pet animals, transport, fruit, farm, restaurant, zoo, birthdays, garden, clothes and the countryside.

First Words In French Teacher's Resource Book

Learning French is fun with the great games and activity sheets in this great book. Topics include: pets, colours, transport, café, supermarket, hobbies, toys and Christmas.

This great book can be used either separately or alongside the stories with the French magician and the French robot.

Photocopiable for class or home use.

Ideal for 3 - 7 year olds.

French

Young Cool Kids Learn French
French Colouring Book For Kids Ages 5 - 7
First Words In French Teacher's Resource Book
Stories for 3-7 year olds: Jack And The French Languasaurus - Books 1, 2 & 3,
Daniel And The French Robot - Books 1, 2 & 3, Sophie And The French Magician
Cool Kids Speak French - Books 1, 2 & 3 *(for kids ages 7 - 11)*
French Word Games - Cool Kids Speak French
Photocopiable Games For Teaching French
40 French Word Searches Cool Kids Speak French
First 100 Words In French Coloring Book Cool Kids Speak French
French at Christmas time
On Holiday In France Cool Kids Speak French
Cool Kids Do Maths In French
Stories in French: Un Alien Sur La Terre, Le Singe Qui Change De Couleur, Tu As Un Animal?

Italian

Young Cool Kids Learn Italian
Italian Colouring Book For Kids Ages 5 - 7
Cool Kids Speak Italian - Books 1, 2 & 3 *(for kids ages 7 - 11)*
Italian Word Games - Cool Kids Speak Italian
Photocopiable Games For Teaching Italian
40 Italian Word Searches Cool Kids Speak Italian
First 100 Words In Italian Coloring Book Cool Kids Speak Italian
On Holiday In Italy Cool Kids Speak Italian
Stories in Italian: Un Alieno Sulla Terra, La Scimmia Che Cambia Colore, Hai Un Animale Domestico?

German

Young Cool Kids Learn German
German Colouring Book For Kids Ages 5 - 7
Sophie And The German Magician *(a story for 3-7 year olds)*
Cool Kids Speak German - Books 1, 2 & 3 *(for kids ages 7 - 11)*
German Word Games - Cool Kids Speak German
Photocopiable Games For Teaching German
40 German Word Searches Cool Kids Speak German
First 100 Words In German Coloring Book Cool Kids Speak German

Spanish

Young Cool Kids Learn Spanish
Spanish Colouring Book For Kids Ages 5 - 7
First Words In Spanish Teacher's Resource Book
Stories for 3-7 year olds: Jack And The Spanish Dinosaur, Sophie And The Spanish Magician,
Daniel And The Spanish Robot - Books 1, 2 & 3
Cool Kids Speak Spanish - Books 1, 2 & 3 *(for kids ages 7 - 11)*
Spanish Word Games - Cool Kids Speak Spanish
Photocopiable Games For Teaching Spanish
40 Spanish Word Searches Cool Kids Speak Spanish
First 100 Words In Spanish Coloring Book Cool Kids Speak Spanish
Spanish at Christmas time
On Holiday In Spain Cool Kids Speak Spanish
Cool Kids Do Maths In Spanish
Stories in Spanish: Un Extraterrestre En La Tierra, El Mono Que Cambia De Color, Seis Mascotas

English as a second language / foreign language

English For Kids Ages 5 - 7
English Colouring Book For Kids Ages 3 - 7
Cool Kids Speak English - Books 1, 2 & 3 *(for kids ages 7 - 11)*
First Words In English - 100 Words To Colour & Learn
English Word Games
Fun Word Search Puzzles

Printed in Great Britain
by Amazon

47864283R00031